Rain

by
Robert Kalan
illustrated by
Donald Crews

Macmillan/McGraw-Hill School Publishing Company

New York   Chicago   Columbus

Macmillan/McGraw-Hill School Division
10 Union Square East
New York, New York 10003

Printed in the United States of America

ISBN 0-02-179093-0 / 1, L. 1

4 5 6 7 8 9   FED   99 98 97 96 95 94 93

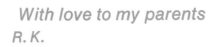

With love to my parents
R. K.

. . . and to mine
D. C.

Blue sky

5

Yellow sun

White clouds

Gray clouds

No sun

RainRain
RainRainRain
RainRainRainRain
InRainRainRainRain
nRainRainRainRain
RainRainRainRainRain
RainRainRainRainRain
RainRainRainRainRain
RainRainRainRain

Gray sky

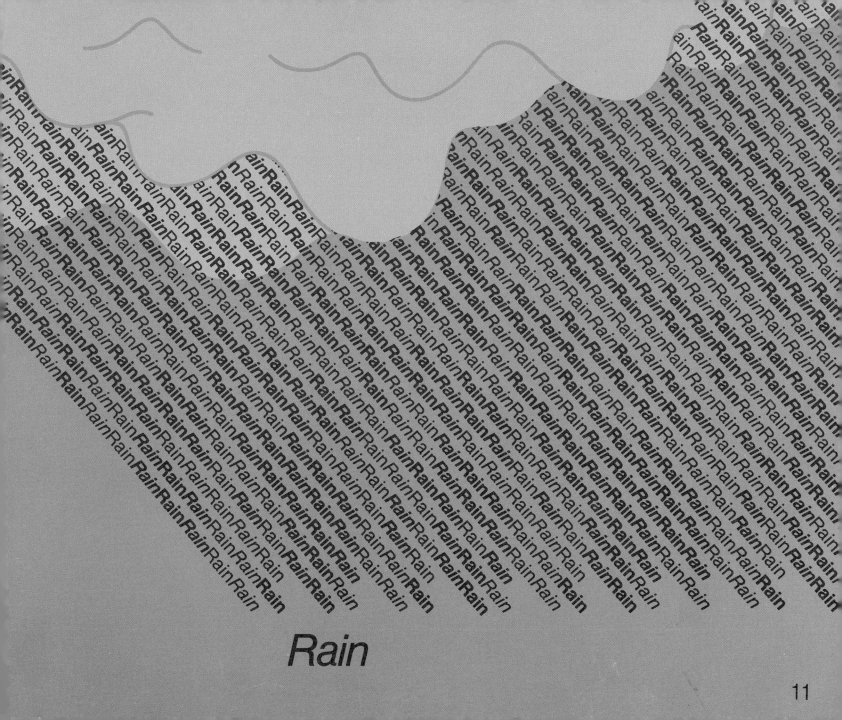

Rain

Rain on the green grass

Rain on the black road

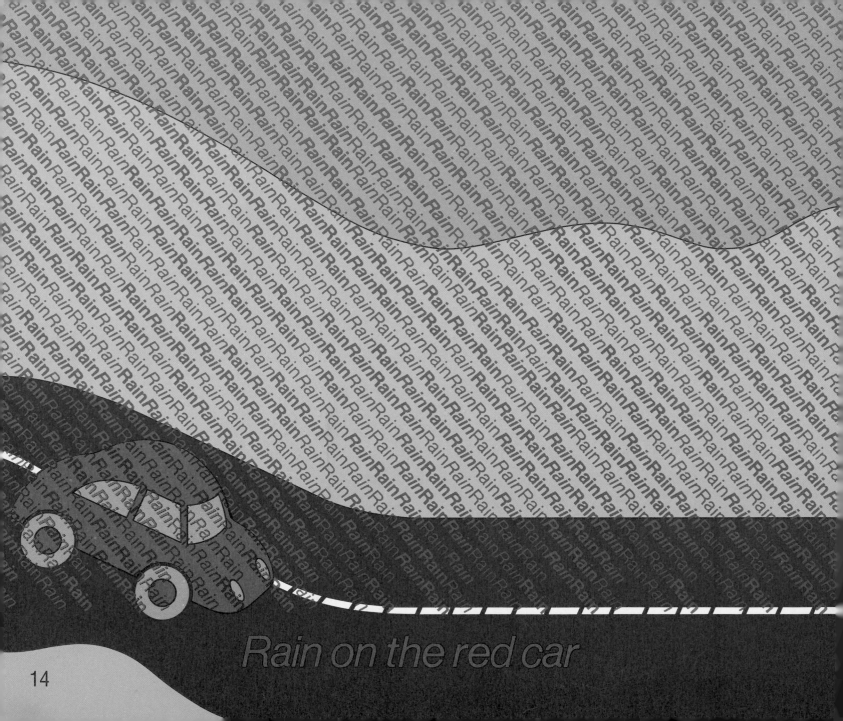

Rain on the red car

14

Rain on the orange flowers

15

Rain on the brown fence

Rain on the purple flowers

Rain on the white house

Rain on the green trees

Rain

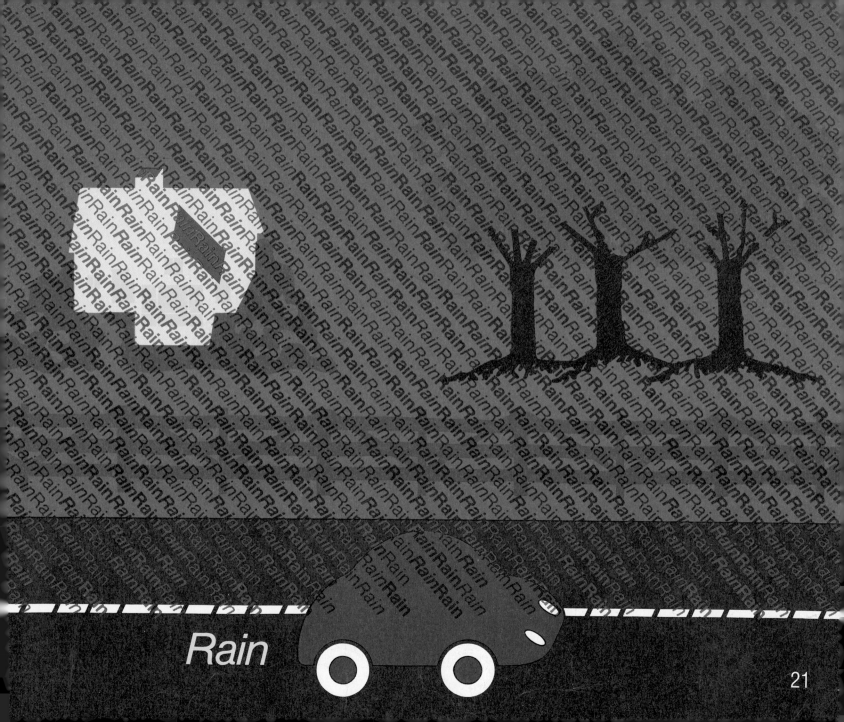

Rain

*RAIN*BOW

ROBERT KALAN was born in Los Angeles. He was graduated from Claremont Men's College.
He has taught reading to both gifted and remedial students as well as kindergarten and fourth grade, and completed a master's degree in education at Claremont Graduate School. He is currently living in Seattle, where he teaches a course in writing for children at the University of Washington.

DONALD CREWS was graduated from Cooper Union for the Advancement of Science and Art in New York City. He has written and illustrated many books for young children, including We Read: A to Z and Ten Black Dots. He and his wife Ann are free-lance artists and designers, and live in New York with their two daughters.